Brain-Boosting
Quantum Puzzles

LAGOON
BOOKS

Series Editor: Sarah Wells

Puzzle Contributors: Rich Garner, Philip Carter,
Bernard Murray, Fran Pickering

Additional Contributors: Ann Marangos,
Peter Sorenti, Lucy Dear, Keely Borthwick

Page Design and Layout: Linley Clode

Cover Design: Alan Shiner

Published by:
LAGOON BOOKS
PO BOX 311, KT2 5QW, UK
PO BOX 990676, Boston, MA 02199, USA

www.lagoongames.com

ISBN: 1902813529

© LAGOON BOOKS, 2001

Printed in Singapore

Brain-Boosting Quantum Puzzles

Introduction

In the same way that physical exercise tones your muscles and makes you fitter, solving puzzles hones your intellect and boosts your IQ.

With this in mind, we have put together a compilation of fun and challenging puzzles, to give you one of the best cerebral workouts ever.

Within this beautifully illustrated book, we bring you nearly 100 of the best quantum puzzles – that is, devilishly difficult logic and math puzzles, that will really put your puzzle-solving skills to the test!

Divided into four chapters, each puzzle has a score of 1, 2 or 3 points.

In **Chapter 1** – you will find the easiest puzzles, ones you should really be able to complete within 60 seconds.

In **Chapter 2** – you will find a slightly more difficult set of puzzles – ones that should be completed within 3 minutes.

In **Chapter 3** – there is a much more difficult range of conundrums, which should take about 5 minutes to crack.

And in **Chapter 4** – you will find the most fiendish puzzles that could take you up to 10 minutes to work out.

If you manage to solve the puzzles within the time limit allocated in each chapter, you can award yourself the points.

A helpful scoring card has been given at the beginning of each chapter to help you to keep score. When you have completed all the chapters, turn to see your overall score on page 191.

For those of you who want to test the theory that practice makes perfect, why not jump to the last chapter of the book and see how you fare? If you solve the puzzle within 10 minutes, congratulations! You really are a puzzle genius. If you do not, however, then go back to the beginning of the book and work through the puzzles in chronological order. By the time you reach Chapter 4, you should have no excuses – your score should have leapt up after all the practice.

If, by the end of the book, you have still not achieved your ultimate goal, and you want more practice, then turn to page 192 to see Lagoon's other Brain-Boosting titles.

Contents

Chapter 1

To score points in this chapter, you need to provide the correct solution to each puzzle within 60 seconds.

To see individual ratings for each puzzle – look under the title of each question. Once you have completed the chapter, turn to page 8, for help adding up your score.

Then turn to page 53 to start chapter 2.

Chapter 1 - Scoring

Puzzle points for correct answer

Animal Magic **2**		A Class Act. **1**
Flower Arrangement. . . . **2**		Garden Game **2**
Temperature Test **1**		Sweet Treat **2**
Chocoholic! **1**		Plot Problem **1**
Relatively Simple **3**		Tick Tock **2**
Shoe Fetish **1**		Climbing Wall **2**
Time Flies. **2**		9 into 10 . . . . **1**
Student Sum **1**		Snookered! **2**
Dice Dilemma **2**		Terrible Trio. **3**
Up, Up and Away **3**		Penny Problem **1**
Sock Shock **2**		Time Crisis **3**

YOUR TOTAL

/ **40**

Animal Magic

Rating 2 Points

In the zoo are a total of 29 tigers and ostriches, all in perfect condition. If these have a total of 92 legs, how many of each are there?

Animal Magic - Solution

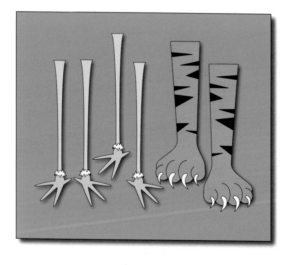

$$
\begin{array}{lll}
17 \text{ tigers} & = & 17 \times 4 = 68 \\
12 \text{ ostriches} & = & 12 \times 2 = \underline{24} \\
& & 92
\end{array}
$$

Flower Arrangement

Rating 2 Points

Mr Sage has a square plot of land divided into nine equal sections. He has daffodil bulbs that will flower in three different colors, and wishes to separate them in his plot as shown. In total he has 15 yellow, 6 white and 6 orange flowering bulbs. It is important to him that he does not have the same number of bulbs in any plots that are adjacent to each other, and he also wants there to be the same number of bulbs in each row and each column. How does he do this, if the highest number of yellow bulbs are in the corner, and the fewest in the right-hand column?

Flower Arrangement - Solution

Temperature Test

Rating 1 Point

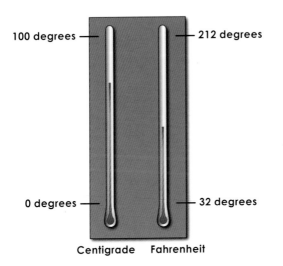

100 degrees — — 212 degrees

0 degrees — — 32 degrees

Centigrade   Fahrenheit

At what temperature do both
thermometers show the same figure?

Temperature Test - Solution

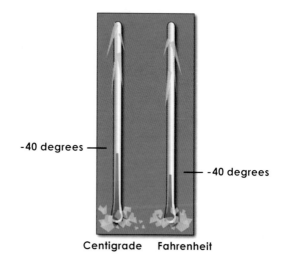

-40 degrees —

— -40 degrees

Centigrade   Fahrenheit

Minus 40 degrees.

Chocoholic!

Rating 1 Point

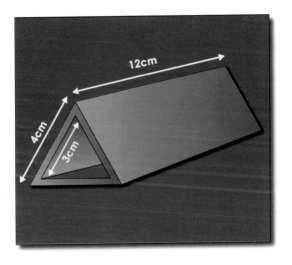

A bar of chocolate, 12cm long, has a cross-section in the shape of an equilateral triangle with sides 4cm. The weight of the whole bar is 8g. A hole is made through the middle of the bar in the form of another equilateral triangle with sides 3cm. What is the weight of the bar now?

Chocoholic! - Solution

3.5g. The weight of the bar is proportional to the
volume, which is the area of the cross section multiplied
by the length. The area of the cross section is
proportional to the square of the length of the side.
Therefore $9/16$ of the volume (and weight)
is removed, and $7/16$ is left. $7/16$ of 8g is 3.5g.

Relatively Simple

Rating 3 Points

The ages of my three uncles, Jim, Alf and Sid total 210. Uncle Sid is a fifth older again than Uncle Alf, and Uncle Alf is a quarter again older than Uncle Jim. How old is each of my uncles?

Relatively Simple - Solution

Jim 56

Alf 70

Sid 84

Shoe Fetish

Rating 1 Point

Imelda is moving house and has packed up her wardrobe. She has blue, green, black and brown shoes, with a ratio of 1 to 2, to 4, to 5 pairs. She's unpacking her wardrobe in a power cut at midnight. How many shoes must she unpack before she can be sure of having a pair?

Shoe Fetish - Solution

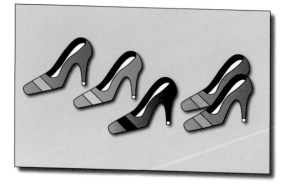

5. The ratio makes no difference – as soon as Imelda has unpacked the fifth shoe, there will be at least one pair of one of the colors.

Time Flies

Rating 2 Points

Two clocks, without any numerical time markings, are fixed to the wall side by side. The first one revolves in a clockwise direction so that in one period of twelve hours it completes one revolution. The second clock moves anti-clockwise at twice the rate of the first clock. They both start off showing identical displays at 12:00, at what time will the clock displays next appear identical again?

Time Flies - Solution

4 o'clock (1600 hours).

Student Sum

Rating 1 Point

Of 2000 students at the University of Sumware,
55% are boys. Of those, 40% are studying science subjects;
of those 75% are first years; of those 60% have
fair hair, and one-third of those regularly attend lectures.
How many boys regularly attend lectures?

Student Sum - Solution

66 boys (as many as that!)

Dice Dilemma

Rating 2 Points

Two dice are numbered differently, and when they are thrown the total of their two uppermost numbers is noted. In order to make as many different totals as possible, what are the lowest numbers that can appear on the dice?

Dice Dilemma - Solution

One dice is numbered 1, 2, 3, 4, 5 and 6. The other dice is numbered 0, 6, 12, 18, 24 and 30. There are 36 different combinations of the dice face, and the numbers 1 to 36 can only be achieved with the dice numbered as shown.

Up, Up and Away

Rating 3 Points

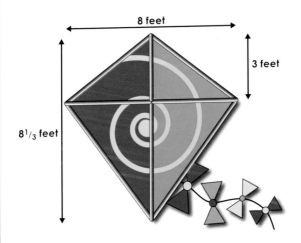

8 feet

3 feet

8 1/3 feet

The framework of a large kite is made up from 8
complete pieces of aluminium linked together as shown.
If the two sections that make up one side of the
kite are formed by congruent triangles (triangles with
the same shape), can the framework be cut from 4
pieces of aluminium that are 10 feet long?

Up, Up and Away - Solution

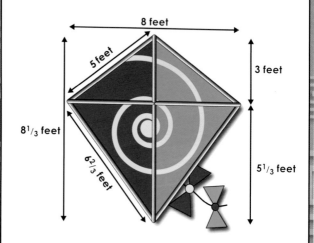

No. An additional two-thirds of a foot of aluminium would be needed. 5ft + 5ft = 1 rod, 3 + 6²/₃ = 1 rod, 4 + 5¹/₃ = 1 rod, leaving 4 and 6²/₃ which cannot be cut from the last rod.

Sock Shock

Rating 2 Points

Gerald has 31 socks in his drawer, 11 identical blue,
8 identical red and 12 identical black. The lights
have fused and he is completely in the dark.
How many socks must he take out to make certain
that he has one pair of each color?

Sock Shock - Solution

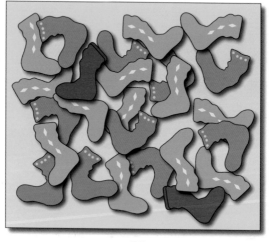

25

If he took out 23 socks they could all be the black
and all the blue socks. To make sure he also
had a pair of red socks he must take out two more.

A Class Act

Rating 1 Point

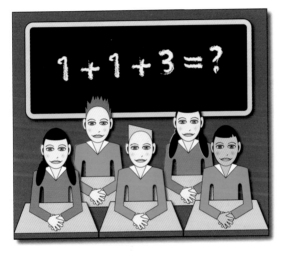

In a class of 30 children aged 8 and 9, there are 50% more girls than boys. There are the same number of boys aged 8 as there are boys aged 9. There are a third more girls aged 8 than there are boys aged 8. How many children in the class are aged 9?

A Class Act - Solution

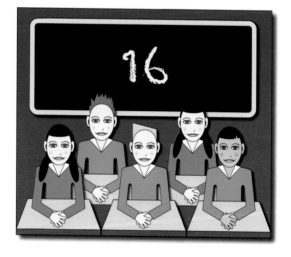

There are 16 children aged 9.
Also:
There are 6 boys aged 8 and 6 boys aged 9.
There are 8 girls aged 8 and 10 girls aged 9.

Garden Game

Rating 2 Points

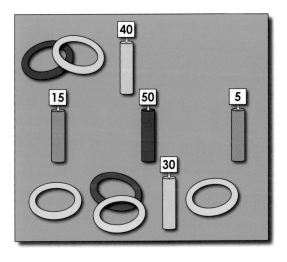

In a game of garden quoits, in which each turn equals four throws, Hani missed on two occasions, but hooped each stick twice. His score doubled from the first to the second throw, and then doubled again from his second to third throw. If he missed on at least one of his first throws, what were his individual scores on each throw?

Garden Game - Solution

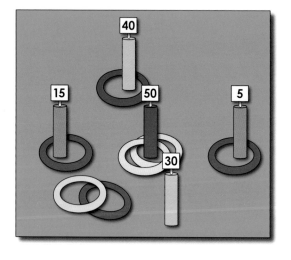

First throw – 5, 5, 30, 0
Second throw – 0, 15, 15, 50
Third throw – 30, 40, 40, 50

Sweet Treat

Rating 2 Points

Sally had twice as many sweets as Jenny, but they each gave 24 away which left Sally with five times as many sweets as Jenny. How many more sweets would Sally have had if they had only given away 16 sweets each?

Sweet Treat - Solution

Sally 48, Jenny 16 (3 times as many).

Plot Problem

Rating 1 Point

Mr Spud is drawing up plans for a new rectangular vegetable plot. He's planning to edge the plot with wooden planks that are exactly 1 metre in length. If he does not want a square plot, what is the smallest number of planks that he would need if numerically he wants to make this number also equal to the area?

Plot Problem - Solution

18 planks, for a plot 3m x 6m (i.e. 18m^2).

Tick Tock

Rating 2 Points

How many minutes before noon is it if 55 minutes ago it was four times as many minutes past 10 a.m.?

Tick Tock - Solution

13 minutes.
12 noon less 13 minutes = 11.47
52 minutes (4 x 13) past 10 a.m. = 10.52
11.47 less 55 minutes = 10.52

Climbing Wall

Rating 2 Points

A wall of bricks is numbered so that each number
is the sum of the numbers in the two bricks immediately
below it. Can you fill in the missing numbers?

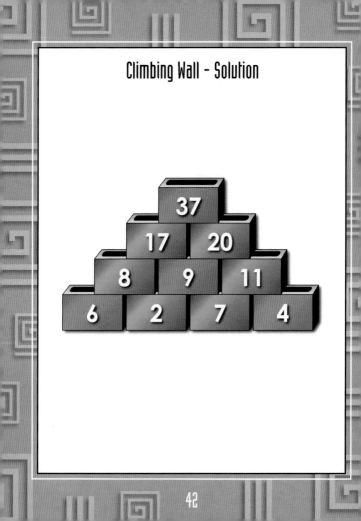

9 into 10

Rating 1 Point

Bill and Ben both have 9 matchsticks each.
Without breaking the matches Bill is able to make
his into 10, but Ben makes his into 28. How?

 TEN

Snookered!

Rating 2 Points

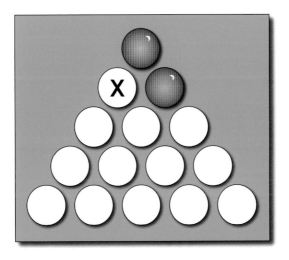

15 snooker balls are assembled into a triangle
as shown. By mistake 8 red and 6 colored balls have been
used instead of all red balls. The values of the balls are
red (1), yellow (2), green (3), brown (4), blue (5)
pink (6) and black (7). If the sum of the values of the
balls for each of the bottom three rows is 10 in all
cases, what is the color of the ball marked X?

Snookered! - Solution

Green.
An example of a possible layout is shown above.
The answer is always green.

Terrible Trio

Rating 3 Points

Complete the grid, using just three
different whole numbers, performing the
calculations in order, left to right.

	+		−		=	4
9	−	3	x	8	=	48
	x		+		=	35

Penny Problem

Rating 1 Point

"Tell me this", said Susie to John, *"Why are 1929 English twopenny pieces worth more than 1928 English twopenny pieces?"*. *"I think they are worth exactly the same"*, replied John. *"Oh no they aren't"*, said Susie. Why was she correct?

Penny Problem - Solution

1929 2 penny pieces are worth 3858 pence, or £38.58 (1929 x 2). 1928 2 penny pieces are worth 3856 pence, or £38.56 (1928 x 2).

Time Crisis

Rating 3 Points

How many minutes is it before 12 noon, if 20 minutes ago it was three times as many minutes past 10 a.m.?

Time Crisis - Solution

25 minutes.
12 noon less 25 minutes = 11.35. 11.35 less 20
minutes = 11.15. 11.15 less 75 minutes (3 x 25) = 10a.m.

Chapter 2

To score points in this chapter, you
need to provide the correct solution to
each puzzle within three minutes.

To see individual ratings for each puzzle –
look under the title of each question.
Once you have completed the chapter, turn
to page 54, for help adding up your score.

Then turn to page 99 to start chapter 3.

Chapter 2 - Scoring

Puzzle points for correct answer

Christmas Decoration . . .	**1**	Train your Brain	. . . .	**1**
Sunflower Power	. . . . . .	**2**	Octahedron.	**2**
Hop Happy	**1**	Roll out the Barrel	. . . . .	**3**
Youngest in the Family . .	**2**	Apples for Storing.	**1**
Triumphant Trumpets . . .	**3**	Bric a Brac	**1**
Boat Race	**2**	Foreign Currency.	**2**
Tropical Fish	**1**	Coal Bunker	**3**
Driving Mad	**1**	A Taxing Problem	**2**
Treasure Hunt	**2**	Number Grid.	**1**
Lorry Worry.	**3**	Wall Wizard	**3**
Production Line.	**2**	Prime Time	**1**

YOUR TOTAL

40

Christmas Decoration

Rating 1 Point

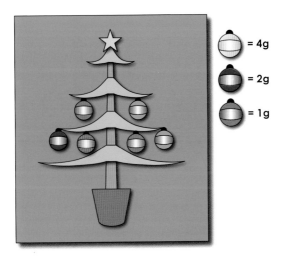

= 4g

= 2g

= 1g

Mary has two more branches to decorate on her Christmas tree. She intends to hang three balls on each branch – a different combination of balls on each branch – but the weight of the balls must balance, so that the branches stay level. If a gold ball weighs 4g, a red ball weighs 2g and a silver ball weighs 1g, how does she decorate the branches?

Christmas Decoration - Solution

= 4g

= 2g

= 1g

Sunflower Power

Rating 2 Points

Flora's garden has three types of sunflower – large yellow, medium orange and small red. The yellow sunflower has one flower head with 12 petals, the orange sunflower has three flower heads each with 14 petals, and the red sunflower has five flower heads each with 13 petals. She has more of the small red plants than either of the others. If there is a total of 617 sunflower petals in her garden, how many of each plant does she have?

Sunflower Power - Solution

3 yellow, 3 orange and 7 red.

Hop Happy

Rating 1 Point

START   FINISH

In its daily routine, a small frog hops around the
lily pads in a square pond, looking for available food,
always starting and ending in the same places.
The frog can only hop from one pad to an adjacent pad,
always visits every pad, and never retraces its steps.
In how many different ways can it do this?

Hop Happy - Solution

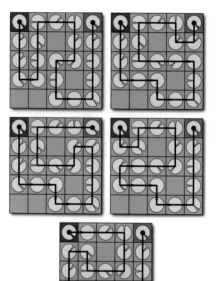

Youngest in the Family

Rating 2 Points

4 generations of the Peters family are posing for a photograph. The different ages, in complete years of the five family members, which total 230, make an arithmetic progression (i.e. they increase by the same amount each time). The difference in age between two of them sitting in the front row is 51. How old is the youngest?

Youngest in the Family - Solution

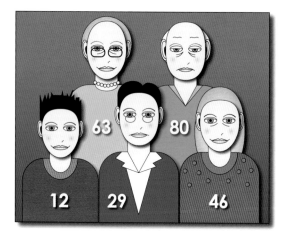

The youngest is 12.
The ages are 12, 29, 46, 63 and 80.

Triumphant Trumpets

Rating 3 Points

A brass band is marching forward in 5 columns and 4 rows, as shown in the diagram. The band includes 4 trumpeters who are scattered among the procession, but with one in each row and situated so that only one trumpeter is equidistant from the other three. Before and after the band turned left, the trumpeter in the right-hand column at the time, is in front of the nearest trumpeter to him. Where are the trumpeters situated?

Triumphant Trumpets - Solution

There are four possible solutions.
One is shown above.

Boat Race

Rating 2 Points

Half way stage

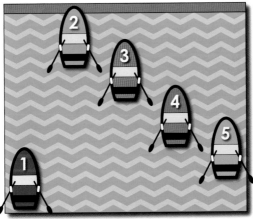

At the halfway stage in a rowing boat race, the positions were as shown. At the finishing post, none of the boats occupied the same position as that at the halfway stage or the same as their boat number. If no boat finished in a position that was next to the position of a boat in an adjacent lane, what was the order of the boats at the finishing line?

Boat Race - Solution

Finish Line

Tropical Fish

Rating 1 Point

In my fish tank I have 34 tiger fish. The male fish have 87 stripes each and the female fish have 29 stripes each. If I take out two-thirds of the male fish, how many stripes in total remain in my fish tank?

Tropical Fish - Solution

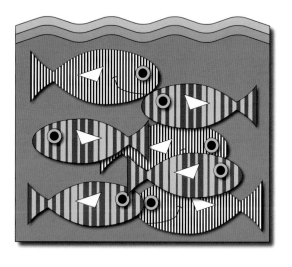

986 stripes.

Driving Mad

Rating 1 Point

Midway through his round of golf, Bob hits a 241 yard drive, which brings his average length per drive for his round (so far), from 205 to 209 yards. How far would he have had to hit the drive to bring his average length of drive up from 205 to 211 yards?

Driving Mad - Solution

259 yards.
8 holes average 205 = 1640 yards
9 holes average 209 = 1881 yards
9 holes average 211 = 1899 yards
1899 − 1640 = 259

Treasure Hunt

Rating 2 Points

2	4	9	6
2	4	8	1
1	4	8	9
6	🧰	3	2

The pirates have found a treasure map with a difference. In order to claim the treasure they must find the starting point and work from square to square horizontally or vertically (but not diagonally) to unravel a meaningful number sequence. Every square must be visited, but only once, and you must finish on the square marked with the treasure.

Treasure Hunt - Solution

The sequence is 6, 12, 24, 48, 96, 192, 384
(doubling up each time)

Lorry Worry

Rating 3 Points

There are a number of new lorries in the manufacturer's factory. There are four types of lorry, with 4 wheels, 6 wheels, 8 wheels, or 12 wheels, and there is an equal number of each. If the total number of wheels is 2730, how many of each type of lorry are there?

Lorry Worry - Solution

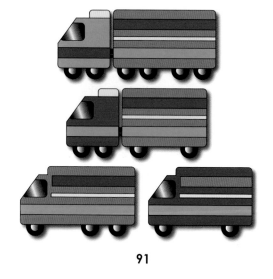

91

Production Line

Rating 2 Points

A car manufacturer produces only red and white models,
which exit the final testing area completely at random.
What are the odds that four consecutive cars of
the same color will exit the test area at any one time?

Production Line - Solution

1 in 8 or 7 to 1.
Each car is red or white = 1 in 2.
To repeat four times is $2^4 = 16$. The first car can
be red or white so the first does not count.
Therefore, the odds are 2^3, or $^7/_1$.

Train your Brain

Rating 1 Point

A 100m long passenger train has to travel through
a tunnel in the Alps that is 8.5 km long. If the
train is travelling at 43km per hour, how long does it
take to pass completely through the tunnel?

Train your Brain - Solution

12 Minutes

Octahedron

Rating 2 Points

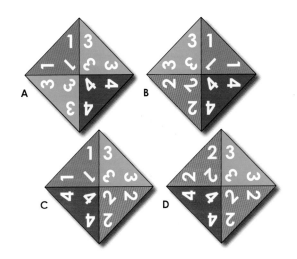

Four different side views of a regular octahedron,
which has 8 equilateral triangular faces
and 6 apexes are shown. What is the total of the
numbers on all 8 faces of the octahedron?

Octahedron - Solution

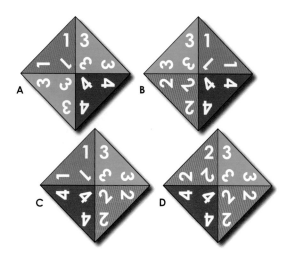

A

B

C

D

22. There are a total of 6 possible views. 2 of the views given must be from completely opposite sides. By studying the layout of the numbers on the views you can deduce that A and D represent opposite sides of the octahedron. The total is therefore the sum of 1, 2, 2, 3, 3, 3, 4 and 4.

Roll out the Barrel

Rating 3 Points

A barrel contains exactly 9 litres of red wine. Max is going to a party and wishes to share 8 litres of wine equally with the seven other partygoers, who all hold 1 litre glasses. Max wants to keep one litre for when he gets home. He only has two other containers that will hold exactly 5 litres and 2 litres respectively. What is the quickest way for him to measure 8 litres into the barrel to take to the party?

Roll out the Barrel - Solution

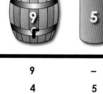

Start	9	–	–
1st pour	4	5	–
2nd pour	4	3	2
3rd pour	6	3	–
4th pour	6	1	2
5th pour	8	1	–

5 pourings. He pours from one container
to another as shown above.

Apples for Storing

Rating 1 Point

George's apple tree produced a bumper crop this year.
Approximately 5% (to the nearest apple) of the
apples were damaged by bugs, 15 apples were damaged
falling off the tree. From the remainder, George
gave a quarter away and stored 48 apples for himself.
How many apples did the tree produce?

Apples for Storing - Solution

83

Bric a Brac

Rating 1 Point

Top view

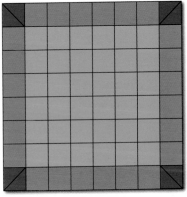

Side view

A small solid toy pyramid is made up of three different shapes of bricks – green solid cubes for the internal base, blue half-size bricks for the sides, and red bricks for the corners. The base of the pyramid is shown. How many more bricks of each size are required to complete the pyramid?

Bric a Brac - Solution

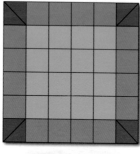

3rd Level
16 green
16 blue
8 red

2nd Level
4 green
8 blue
8 red

Top Level
8 red

20 green, 24 blue and 24 red.

Foreign Currency

Rating 2 Points

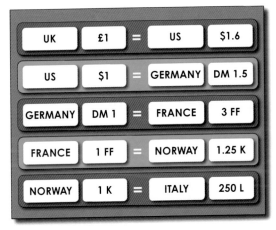

UK	£1	=	US	$1.6
US	$1	=	GERMANY	DM 1.5
GERMANY	DM 1	=	FRANCE	3 FF
FRANCE	1 FF	=	NORWAY	1.25 K
NORWAY	1 K	=	ITALY	250 L

An English businessman went on an international trip. He carried an emergency cash fund of £100, which he exchanged to local currency in each country. His travels necessitated the exchanges shown. On his way to Rome airport, his hire car broke down and the garage insisted on a cash payment of 210,000 lire. Did he have enough to pay to have his car mended?

Foreign Currency - Solution

Yes, he had 225,000 lire.

Coal Bunker

Rating 3 Points

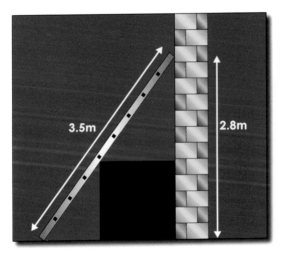

3.5m

2.8m

A ladder that is 3.5 metres long is rested against a coal bunker that is as high as it is wide and reaches exactly 2.8 metres up a vertical wall, as shown. How wide is the coal bunker?

Coal Bunker - Solution

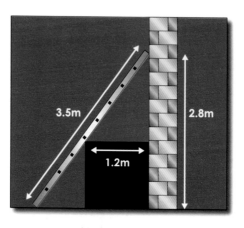

1.2 metres.
Let the width of the coal bunker be x metres.
The distance of the foot of the ladder from the wall is
2.1 metres (obtained by Pythagoras's theorem, the typical
3, 4, 5 triangle, distance squared = 3.5 squared minus
2.8 squared, i.e. 12.25 – 7.84 = 4.41 and the square root of
4.41 is 2.1). The triangle formed by the whole construction
is similar in shape to the small triangle at the base
of the ladder, therefore (2.1 – x) ÷ x = 2.1 ÷ 2.8, which
gives 2.8(2.1 – x) = 2.1 x or 5.88 = 4.9 x and x = 1.2

A Taxing Problem

Rating 2 Points

In the land of Laguna, income tax is paid on income earned every month at the rate of 5% on the first 500 Dubloons and then at 8% on the balance. Harry has just returned, at the end of a month, from a 4-week holiday, to discover that he owes 1,145 Dubloons in tax. How much income does he need to earn in the next month to pay all his income tax and have 250 Dubloons left over to spend?

A Taxing Problem - Solution

1,500 Dubloons

If he earns K Dubloons, then K minus
the tax on K is equal to 1,145 + 250.

The tax on K is 500 x .05 + (K - 500) x 0.08,
which is 25 + 0.08K – 40 = 0.08K –15.

Therefore K – (0.08K – 15) = 1,395,
i.e. 0.92K = 1,380 and K = 1,500

Number Grid

Rating 1 Point

Can you complete the above grid
using different numbers?

Number Grid - Solution

$$6 + 5 = 11$$

$$4 \div 1 = 4$$

$$6 \times 4 = 24$$

$$5 + 1 = 6$$

Wall Wizard

Rating 3 Points

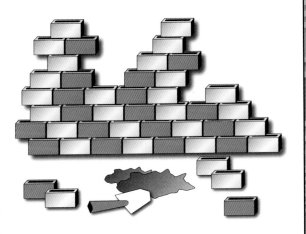

If a man and a half build a wall and a half in a day and a half, how many walls will 9 men build in 9 days?

Wall Wizard - Solution

1 man builds $2/3$ of a wall in a day.
Therefore, 9 men would build $18/3$ = 6 walls
a day, or 54 walls in 9 days.

Prime Time

Rating 1 Point

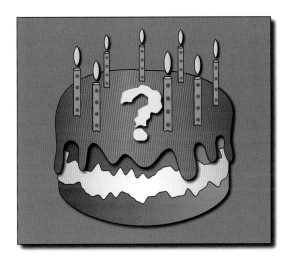

Gerald is in his twenties and next to prime. At half his age he was not between primes. When he is double his current age he will also be next to prime. When he is treble his current age he will sit between two primes. How old is Gerald?

Prime Time - Solution

Chapter 3

To score points in this chapter, you
need to provide the correct solution to
each puzzle within five minutes.

To see individual ratings for each puzzle –
look under the title of each question.
Once you have completed the chapter, turn
to page 100, for help adding up your score.

Then turn to page 145 to start chapter 4.

Chapter 3 - Scoring

Puzzle points for correct answer

The Lions of Laguna	**3**	100m Dash	**1**
Roosting Birds	**1**	Tunnel Teaser	**1**
The Queen's Jam Tarts	**3**	In the Park	**2**
Rat Catcher	**1**	Pyramid Problem	**2**
Superbowl!	**2**	Gridlock	**3**
Shopping Spree	**1**	Candle Conundrum	**1**
Newt's Law	**2**	Hopscotch	**2**
Weights and Measures	**2**	Attendance Record	**1**
Easy Rider	**1**	A Puzzling Sum	**3**
Place Your Bets!	**2**	Money Lender	**2**
Twice the Fun	**3**	Mrs Bloomer	**1**

YOUR TOTAL

/ **40**

The Lions of Laguna

Rating 3 Points

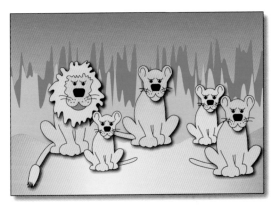

In the Laguna game reserve there are 63 lions, divided equally between three prides, Bigroar, Darkmane and Catanga, each with lions, lionesses and cubs. There are 3 times more lionesses than (adult male) lions, and in each of Bigroar and Darkmane there are 50% more lionesses than in Catanga. There are fewer (adult male) lions in Darkmane than in either of the other prides. None of the prides had 4 more, or more than 4 more cubs than those in either of the other prides, and none of the prides had the same number of cubs. How many lions, lionesses and cubs are there in each pride?

The Lions of Laguna - Solution

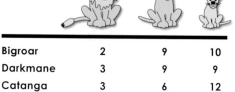

Bigroar	2	9	10
Darkmane	3	9	9
Catanga	3	6	12

Roosting Birds

Rating 1 Point

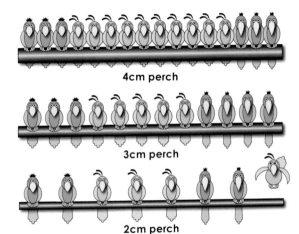

4cm perch

3cm perch

2cm perch

The strength of the perches in a birdcage are proportional
to their thickness. Three species of bird, yellow canaries,
blue budgies and green finches sit on the perches
as shown in the diagram above. A yellow canary flies
in to settle on the 2cm perch and it starts to bend.
Which species of bird is the heaviest?

Roosting Birds - Solution

The budgies

Let b, c and f represent the weights of a budgie, canary and finch respectively. Compare the proportionate weights of the birds on the 2cm perch with those on the 3cm and 4cm perches in turn, by multiplying the birds sitting on the 2cm perch plus the canary by 1.5 and 2 respectively.

The Queen's Jam Tarts

Rating 3 Points

I do not know who stole the tarts.

Alfred

I know who stole the tarts.

Harold

I know a guard, who is not myself, who does not know who stole the tarts

Julian

Guard Julian did not steal the tarts.

Tristan

Four guards were patrolling the rooms of the palace, when it was discovered that some of the Queen's jam tarts had been stolen from the kitchen. One of the guards confided his indiscretion to one of the others without either of the other two guards knowing. Two of the guards tell the truth and two of the guards lie. From their statements can you work out which guard stole the tarts?

The Queen's Jam Tarts - Solution

Julian

Guard Julian stole the tarts.

Rat Catcher

Rating 1 Point

In the rat-infested village of Cattatackya last month,
each cat killed the same number of rats as every other cat.
The total number of rat fatalities during the month
came to 2923. Less than 50 cats achieved
this remarkable feat. How many cats were there in
Cattatackya, and how many rats did each kill?

Rat Catcher - Solution

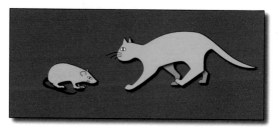

79 Rats　　　　　　**37 Cats**

37 cats each killed 79 rats.
2923 is the product of the two prime numbers
37 and 79, making the answer a unique one.

Superbowl!

Rating 2 Points

Nine members of the American football team
were lined up waiting to take their place on the
playing field. If two players in the top row changed places
with two players on the second row, then the number
formed by the players on the bottom row would be
exactly a fifth of the number formed by the five players on
the top row. Can you work out which two players on the
top row, and which two players on the second row,
need to change places for this to occur?

Superbowl! - Solution

7 and 3 from the top row need to change places with 4 and 6 from the bottom row.

Shopping Spree
Rating 1 Point

Out of 100 ladies surveyed leaving Macy's department store, 95 had bought an item of clothing, 75 had coffee in the café, 80 had bought jewellery and 70 had bought cosmetics. How many, at least, must have had all four items?

Shopping Spree - Solution

25 Women

Add the numbers together, which gives 95 + 75 + 80 + 70 = 325 among 100 ladies. This gives 3 items to each, and 4 items to 25 of these ladies. The least number of ladies to have had all 4 items is, therefore, 25.

Newt's Law

Rating 2 Points

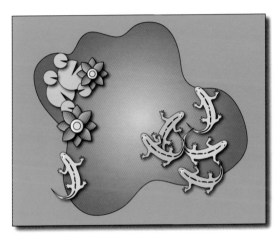

Every newt in the lagoon is a hermaphrodite, and will
produce 2 offspring exactly one year after it is itself born,
and a newt will not move away from a pond after
having offspring. Six years ago a newt moved to
a new pond within a few hours of being born, where it
was the only inhabitant. There are now a total of
98 newts in this new pond. If all newts survived, and
none had moved away during the last year,
how many had moved away over the 6 years?

Newt's Law - Solution

3 newts had moved away.

If all the newts had stayed every year, there would be a total of 127 in the pond. However 29 are missing.

One newt moved away during the fourth year = 15 newts missing (1 + 2 + 4 + 8)

Two newts moved away during the fifth year = 14 newts missing (1 + 2 + 4) x 2

Weights and Measures

Rating 2 Points

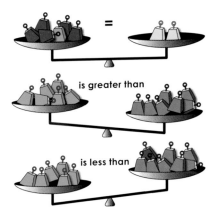

is greater than

is less than

Mr Candy, the sweet shop owner has bought a set of weights that are in different whole units of grams, none greater than 10. He discovers that the number of grams are not printed on the weights, instead they are painted different colors according to their weight. Can you help him to calculate the value of the blue weight?

Weights and Measures - Solution

The blue weight is 5 grams.
Also:
Green = 6 grams
Red = 2 grams
Yellow = 8 grams

Easy Rider

Rating 1 Point

A motorbike travels 100 miles at a speed of 40mph. Its fuel consumption is 80 miles per gallon, and its tank has a capacity of 3 gallons. At the start of the journey, the tank is full but has a leak. When the destination is reached, the tank is empty. How much fuel is leaking per hour?

Easy Rider - Solution

0.7 gallons

Place Your Bets!

Rating 2 Points

$24 $30 $42 $46
$52 $78 $94 $104 $130

Tom, Dick and Harry each won on the horses for three days running. The bookkeeper paid out sums of $130, $104, $94, $78, $52, $46, $42, $30, $24. Tom won twice as much as Dick. What was the total winning amount for each man over the three days?

Place your Bets! - Solution

Tom wins $52 + $78 + $94 = $224
Dick wins $24 + $46 + $42 = $112
Harry wins $30 + $104 + $130 = $264

Twice the Fun

Rating 3 Points

Mr Smith has 4 children, two of whom are twins. The age of the oldest child is three times the age of the youngest, and two of the ages are just one year apart. If the total of the ages of all four children is five times greater than the middle age, what is the age of the twins?

Twice the Fun - Solution

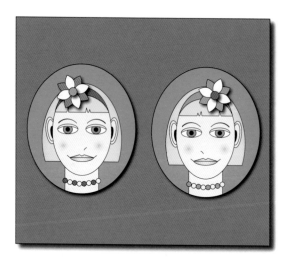

The twins are 4.
There are 2 possible age combinations for the children –
3, 4, 4, 9 or 9, 4, 4, 5. Either way, the twins are still 4.

100m Dash

Rating 1 Point

Frank, Greg, Harry, Irving and Joseph are the competitors in a 100 metre race. Frank beat Greg by as many places as Irving beat Joseph. Neither Harry nor Joseph was third or fifth. In what order did they finish?

100m Dash - Solution

Harry, Irving, Frank, Joseph and Greg

Harry, Irving, Frank, Joseph and Greg

Tunnel Teaser

Rating 1 Point

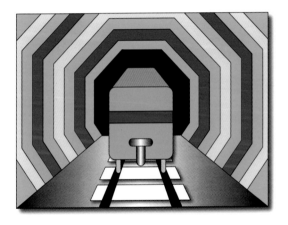

A train travelling at a speed of 55mph enters a tunnel that is 2.5 miles long. The length of the train is 0.25 miles. How long does it take for all of the train to pass through the tunnel, from the moment the front enters, to the moment the rear emerges?

Tunnel Teaser - Solution

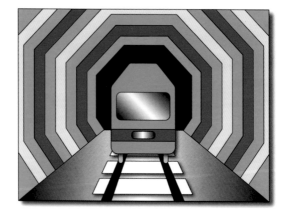

3 minutes

In the Park

Rating 2 Points

A square park is denoted by its North, East, South and West sides. It has 2 seats on each side. The seats north and south sit a maximum of 4 people each and the seats east and west sit a maximum of 3 people each. Two seats are full. One seat has no-one sitting on it. No seats next to or opposite each other have the same number of people sitting on them. The total of people in the SE corner equals the total of people in the NW corner, but none of the seats has the same number of people on them. The total of people in the NE corner was double that in the SW corner. How many people are sitting on the seats in the park?

In the Park - Solution

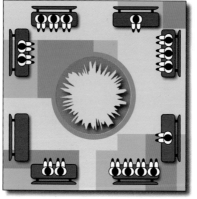

16 people are sitting on the seats in the park.
One possible arrangement is shown. There are several
arrangements, but the total will always be 16.

Pyramid Problem

Rating 2 Points

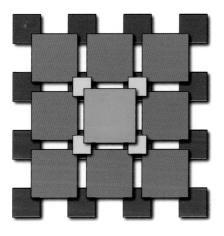

A pyramid has 16 cubes as its base, with each brick being 16cm in length and 16cm from the bricks next to it. 9 cubes are placed symmetrically on top of this base, 4 cubes are placed symmetrically on top of these, with finally 1 cube in the middle on top. In each case, every cube has one-ninth of its base area resting on the 4 cubes immediately below it. What is the height of the pyramid?

Pyramid Problem - Solution

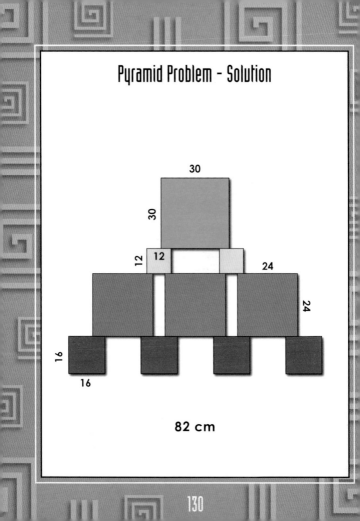

82 cm

Gridlock

Rating 3 Points

?	+	?	÷	?	=	3
÷		x		÷		
?	+	?	÷	?	=	4
+		÷		+		
?	x	?	÷	?	=	2

=   =   =

3   **4**   **3**

Using just two different numbers, complete
the grid, performing the calculations in order,
left to right and top to bottom.

Gridlock - Solution

4	+	2	÷	2	=	3
÷		X		÷		
4	+	4	÷	2	=	4
+		÷		+		
2	X	2	÷	2	=	2
=		=		=		
3		4		3		

Candle Conundrum

Rating 1 Point

**20 cm high
6 cm diameter**

**30 cm high
4 cm diameter**

The two candles shown in the diagram above are made
of exactly the same material, and are lit at exactly the
same time. They both burn an equal volume of material at
the same rate. At what height will they be equal?

Candle Conundrum - Solution

12 cm high

The volume of each candle is calculated using
the equation $\pi r^2 h$ (where h = height).

Hopscotch

Rating 2 Points

Professor Haggis is devising a new game of hopscotch to help the children with their maths. She has almost finished marking out the grid and has just one number to chalk in. What should the number be?

Hopscotch - Solution

The numbers formed in the center are arrived at
by multiplying together the numbers on the outside.
So 6 x 3 = 18, 8 x 6 = 48, 3 x 8 = 24 and 3 x 7 = 21.

Attendance Record

Rating 1 Point

During the first week of the ice hockey season, the attendance figures from Monday to Friday decreased every day, and on each day, the attendance figure was a palindrome (i.e. reads the same backwards as forwards). All of the digits from 0 to 9 appeared, but none of them on more than one day. The smallest attendance of 464 happened on Friday, and the difference between the attendance figures on Monday and Tuesday was 11. The total attendance over the 5 days was 8888. What was the attendance on Thursday?

Attendance Record - Solution

878

The attendance figure for Thursday was 878.
Also:
Monday – 3003
Tuesday – 2992
Wednesday – 1551

A Puzzling Sum

Rating 3 Points

$$8152 + 1919$$
$$6182 + 9019$$

If the first two numbers total 8679, what is the total of the second set of numbers?

A Puzzling Sum - Solution

6161 + 2518

6106 + 2819

8925.
Turn the page upside down and
add the numbers together!

Money Lender

Rating 2 Points

Five brothers all applied for loans of different values. Andy's loan was $75,000 larger than Brian's, which was $45,000 less than Jon's. Jon in turn had been loaned $15,000 more than Eddie, who had borrowed $15,000 more than Dave. The sum of Brian and Eddie's loans was $120,000. What was the value of the loan taken out by each brother?

Money Lender - Solution

Andy: $120,000
Brian: $45,000
Jon: $90,000
Dave: $60,000
Eddie: $75,000

Mrs Bloomer

Rating 1 Point

Mrs Bloomer has a large number of small pentagonal shaped serving plates that have spaces for 5 serving portions and a dip in the center. As well as the dip, there are only 4 different items, carrot slices, cucumber strips, breadsticks and potato chips to serve and she wishes to ensure that all plates have all 4 items, but that an item does not appear next to an identical item. How many guests can she entertain at the dinner table if all the plates have a different presentation? (Rotations of plates can be ignored).

Mrs Bloomer - Solution

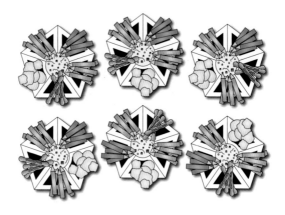

23 guests.

One item of food must appear twice on every serving.

A = carrot, B = cucumber, C = breadsticks, D = potato chips.

A appears twice, 6 times, as shown above.

Similarly B, C and D each appear twice
6 times, giving a total of 24 presentations – 1 for
Mrs Bloomer and 23 for her guests.

Chapter 4

To score points in this chapter, you need to provide the correct solution to each puzzle within ten minutes.

To see individual ratings for each puzzle – look under the title of each question. Once you have completed the chapter, turn to page 146, for help adding up your score.

Then turn to page 191 to see how you fared overall in the Brain-Boosting Quantum Puzzle Challenge.

Chapter 4 - Scoring

Puzzle points for correct answer

Rope Bridge Problem . . .	**2**	Postal Problem	**1**
Riding Tandem	**3**	Mechanical Mayhem.	**1**
Cross Number	**1**	Evaporation Enigma	**2**
Cooking up Trouble	**1**	Bedtime Bother.	**1**
Cats and Dogs.	**2**	Figure it Out	**1**
Letter Link.	**2**	In the Square	**3**
Fun Run.	**1**	Space Station	**3**
Piece of Cake	**2**	Screwy Problem.	**2**
Math Mayhem	**3**	More Magic Squares	**1**
Half Measures.	**2**	Potty Problem	**3**
Magic Squares.	**2**	Number Crunching	**1**

YOUR TOTAL

/ **40**

Rope Bridge Problem

Rating 2 Points

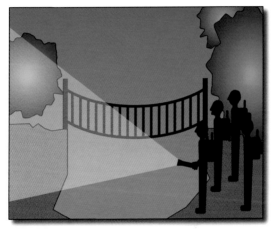

Four explorers in the jungle have to cross a rope bridge at midnight. The bridge is only strong enough to support two people at a time. Between them they only have one torch, which they need to be able to cross the bridge. Thomas can cross the bridge in 4 minutes, his sister Sarah can cross the bridge in 7 minutes, their father Charles can cross in 11 minutes, but old Colonel Montmorency can only hobble across in 18 minutes. How quickly is it possible for all four explorers to reach the other side?

Rope Bridge Problem - Solution

43 Minutes

First Thomas and Sarah cross: 7 minutes
Then Thomas returns: 4 minutes
Then Charles and Colonel Montmorency cross: 18 minutes
Then Sarah returns : 7 minutes
Finally Thomas and Sarah cross : 7 minutes

Riding Tandem

Rating 3 Points

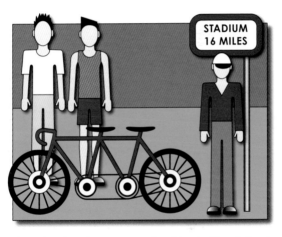

Three brothers have one tandem bicycle. They intend to watch a football match that starts at 3pm, and decide to share the walking and cycling. The twins cycle at 12mph alone, and together at 16mph. David cycles at 9mph alone and at 15mph with one of the twins. The twins walk at 5mph. David will not walk at all. At what time should they leave home, allowing 5 minutes for cycle changeovers and entry into the stadium, assuming they are aiming to arrive in the quickest time possible?

Riding Tandem - Solution

They should set out at 1:04pm, taking 1 hour
51 minutes + 5 minutes to get there.

David cycles with twin A to a suitable point, S, say, while
twin B starts walking. Twin A gets off to walk the rest of
the way to T. David returns to collect twin B at R, say.
Compare distance and time travelled to R, R to S and S to T.
Note that each twin walks the same distance and David
jointly cycles the whole way plus twice between R and S.

Cross Number

Rating 1 Point

?	+	?	÷	?	=	3
×		+		+		+
?	−	?	+	4	=	?
−		÷		−		÷
?	−	2	−	?	=	?
=		=		=		=
5	+	?	−	?	=	?

Insert the remaining numbers into the grid so that
all calculations are correct reading both across and down.
All numbers to be inserted are less than 10.

Cross Number - Solution

6	+	9	÷	5	=	3
x		+		+		+
2	−	1	+	4	=	5
−		÷		−		÷
7	−	2	−	1	=	4
=		=		=		=
5	+	5	−	8	=	2

Cooking up Trouble

Rating 1 Point

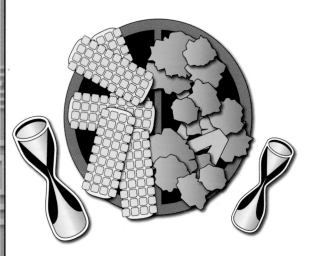

Mrs Bretton is cooking sweetcorn and broccoli in the same pan with dual containers. She realizes that she does not have a clock available, but does have two glass timers, one that takes 4 minutes and the other that takes 7 minutes. She wants to boil the sweetcorn for 10 minutes and the broccoli for 15 minutes. How does she do it?

Cooking up Trouble - Solution

Calling the 4 minute timer (F) and the 7 minute timer (S) Mrs Bretton proceeds as follows:

Time 0 minutes	When the water boils start both timers.
Time 4 minutes	(F) runs out. Turn over (F).
Time 7 minutes	(S) runs out. Turn over (S) and turn over (F), which now has 3 min to run.
Time 10 minutes	(F) runs out. Turn over (F) and turn over (S), which has 3 min to run. Remove sweetcorn.
Time 13 minutes	(S) runs out. Turn over (S) and turn over (F), which now has 1 min to run.
Time 14 minutes	(F) runs out. Turn over (S), which now has 1 min to run.
Time 15 minutes	(S) runs out. Remove broccoli.

Cats and Dogs

Rating 2 Points

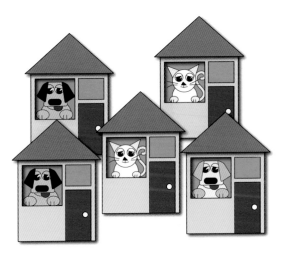

In the village of Hambledown 70% of the houses
had at least one cat and 60% had at least one dog.
There were 20 houses without any pets and 80
houses with at least one cat and at least one dog.
How many houses were there in the village?

Cats and Dogs - Solution

200 houses

200 houses.
Houses with cats only = 60
Houses with dogs only = 40
Houses with cats and dogs = 80
Houses with no pets = 20

Letter Link

Rating 2 Points

LOG = 12

BOSS = 27

EMBLEM = 23

GAMES = 11

BOOKS = 37

LAGOON = ?

In the diagram, each letter represents one of the numbers 0 to 9, added together to give the totals shown. Can you work out how much LAGOON is worth?

Letter Link - Solution

S = 5

O = 8

B = 9

G = 0

L = 4

A = 1

K = 7

N = 6

E = 2 or 3

M = 2 or 3

Lagoon is worth 27.

Fun Run

Rating 1 Point

Harvey recently took part in the annual fun run for
the guards of Laguna. All managed to complete the course
and Harvey was positioned somewhere in the top half.
It was noted that if 10 more guards had finished in front
of him rather than behind him he would have been
first in the bottom half. However, if 6 of those in front
of him had finished behind him he would have
just crept into the top 10%. How many guards took
part in the run and where did Harvey finish?

Fun Run - Solution

36. Harvey finished 9th.

x = guards that finished in front of Harvey
y = guards that finished behind Harvey

Note that there are x + y + 1 guards in total and evaluate
from the information given, bearing in mind that
only whole numbers of guards apply to the top 10%.

Piece of Cake

Rating 2 Points

Flora is baking cakes. She's set herself a challenge
to ice the cakes with numbers 1 to 9,
with the numbers arranged in such a way that:

**Numbers 1 and 2 and all the
digits between them add up to 21**

**Numbers 2 and 3 and all the
digits between them add up to 12**

**Numbers 3 and 4 and all the
digits between them add up to 24**

**Numbers 4 and 5 and all the digits
between them add up to 25.**

(The numbers do not have to appear in ascending order).

Piece of Cake - Solution

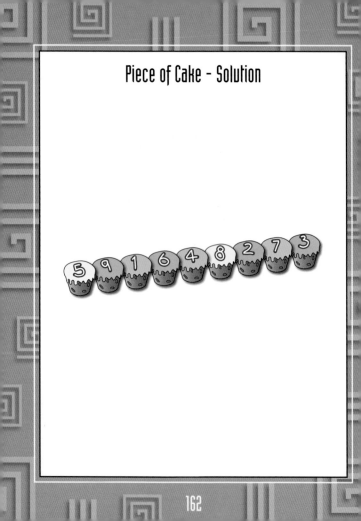

Math Mayhem

Rating 3 Points

11 16 18

19 21 24

26 29 31

Laura teaches math to young children in the morning and teenagers in the evening. She puts five different numbers on the board and asks the youngsters to add together any three. She puts these answers on the board, and removes the five original numbers. In the evening she asks the teenagers to work out what the original numbers were. One bright student states that there are ten different ways to add together five numbers, but that there are only nine on the board. Laura confirms that all the possible numbers are included. What were the original five numbers?

Math Mayhem - Solution

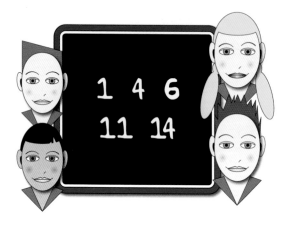

1 4 6
11 14

From the information given, one of the obtained numbers appears twice. Let the original numbers be a, b, c, d and e. Sum these in threes. The 1st, 2nd, 9th and 10th can be defined but the others could be a choice of two of the sums, e.g. 18 may be (a + b + e) or (a + c + d). Evaluate.

$$1 + 4 + 6 = 11, \quad 1 + 4 + 11 = 16,$$
$$1 + 6 + 11 = 18, \quad 1 + 4 + 14 = 19, \quad 1 + 6 + 14 = 21,$$
$$4 + 6 + 11 = 21, \quad 4 + 6 + 14 = 24, \quad 1 + 11 + 14 = 26,$$
$$4 + 11 + 14 = 29, \quad 6 + 11 + 14 = 31.$$

Half Measures

Rating 2 Points

Draw just one line to divide the circle into two equal halves so that the numbers in each half add up to the same total.

Half Measures - Solution

150 in each half.

Magic Squares

Rating 2 Points

23	6	19	2	15
4	12	25	8	16
10	18	11	14	22
1	24	7	20	3
17	5	13	21	9

25	10	3	6	11
22	12	19	8	4
1	9	13	17	15
2	18	7	14	24
5	16	23	20	21

Here are two incomplete magic number squares
in which only some of the horizontal, vertical and diagonal
lines total 65. However, by swapping just three
numbers in the left-hand square with three numbers
in the right-hand square it is possible to create
two magic squares where all lines total 65.

Magic Squares - Solution

23	6	19	2	15
4	12	25	8	16
10	18	1	14	22
11	24	7	20	3
17	5	13	21	9

25	10	3	6	21
22	12	19	8	4
11	9	13	17	15
2	18	7	14	24
5	16	23	20	1

Postal Problem

Rating 1 Point

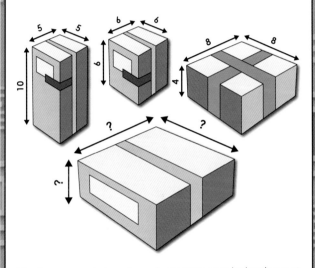

The Laguna postal service only accepts parcels that have at least one square side. What is more, when measured in inches, if the volume (X cubic inches) is the same as the total surface area (X square inches) no charge at all is made for postage. There are four parcel sizes that fit this bill, three are (6 x 6 x 6), (5 x 5 x 10) and (8 x 8 x 4). Can you find the other one that has a value for X of 432?

Postal Problem - Solution

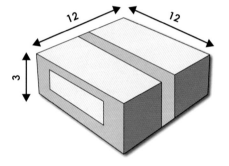

Calculate the volume and surface area of
a parcel measuring a inches by a inches by b inches.
Equate these to 432 and eliminate b.
Solve for a by inspection and trial and error.

Mechanical Mayhem

Rating 1 Point

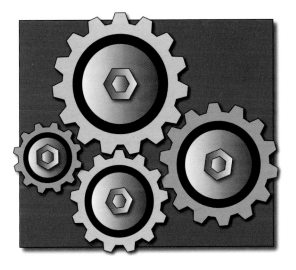

An industrial machine has four cogs that are meshed together. The largest cog has 15 teeth, the next 14 teeth, the next 13 teeth and the smallest has 12 teeth. How many revolutions must the largest cog make before all cogs return to their original positions?

Mechanical Mayhem - Solution

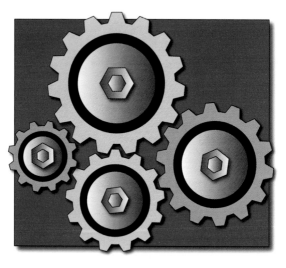

364 revolutions

Prime numbers are used to determine the smallest
number of revolutions of the largest cog to
enable them all to return to their original positions.

Evaporation Enigma

Rating 2 Points

VAT A
Exposed to
atmosphere at
1500 hours
All liquid
evaporated at
1542 hours.

VAT B
Exposed to
atmosphere at
1500 hours
All liquid
evaporated at
1600 hours.

VAT C
Exposed to
atmosphere at
1500 hours
All liquid
evaporated at
1630 hours.

Professor Gribb has invented a new liquid fuel.
When exposed to the atmosphere it evaporates at a
constant rate. He has made two modifications to the liquid
that have progressively slowed the rate of evaporation and
he wishes to test these against the original. He puts the
fuels into 3 different-sized vats. vat B is 4cm taller than
vat C. At 1530 hours the level of the liquid in all three vats
was the same. Assuming all the vats were originally filled
to the brim, can you calculate the height of vat A?

Evaporation Enigma - Solution

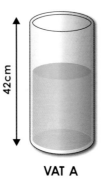

VAT A

42cm.
Comparing the rates of evaporation in vats B and
C will give their heights as 16cm and 12cm.
The liquid in vat A evaporates at the rate of 1cm
per minute (12cm ÷ 12min), therefore in 42
minutes 42cm will have evaporated.

Bedtime Bother

Rating 1 Point

At 2.00pm Mary's clock is showing the correct time, but thereafter it loses 17 minutes every hour. Later on, Mary gets tired and goes up to bed, only to see 8.27pm on the clock. Surely it's not that early! Actually, the clock stopped an hour ago. What is the correct time?

Bedtime Bother - Solution

12 midnight.

Figure it Out

Rating 1 Point

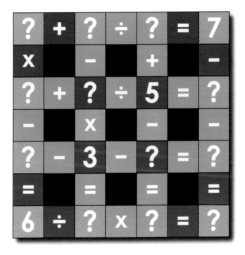

Insert the remaining numbers into the grid so that
all calculations are correct reading both across and down.
All numbers to be inserted are less than 10.

Figure it Out - Solution

5	+	9	÷	2	=	7
x		−		+		−
3	+	7	÷	5	=	2
−		x		−		−
9	−	3	−	4	=	2
=		=		=		=
6	÷	6	x	3	=	3

In the square

Rating 3 Points

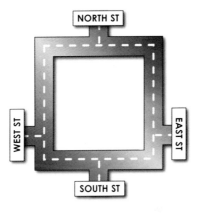

NORTH ST

WEST ST

EAST ST

SOUTH ST

Tom drives into Central Square. The first house on his left is number 1. Apart from the four roads, which all have exactly the same width as a house frontage, the square is surrounded by identical detached houses, numbered consecutively in a clockwise direction. North and South Street are positioned centrally opposite each other. East and West Street are opposite each other with their northerly side exactly one-third of the way along the road. Tom drives clockwise round the square and as he leaves the square the last house on his left is number 73. How many houses are there, and what route did he take?

In the square - Solution

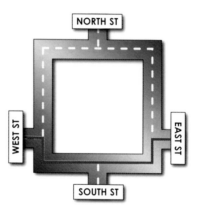

There are 176 houses. Tom entered via
East Street and left via West Street.

Let m be the number of houses in one half
of the South/North sides. There are 2m (houses)
on each side, and 8m in total.

Let n be the number of houses to the south of East/West St.
There are therefore 2(n + 1) on their north sides.

Therefore n+2(n + 1) = 2m, i.e. 3n + 2 = 2m.

Establishing the number of houses between each of
the 16 entry and exit points in terms of m and n and
inspecting possibilities gives n = 14 and m = 22.

Space Station

Rating 3 Points

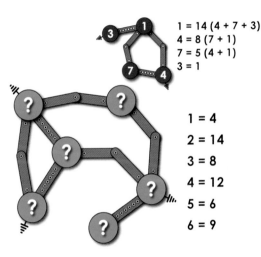

$1 = 14 (4 + 7 + 3)$
$4 = 8 (7 + 1)$
$7 = 5 (4 + 1)$
$3 = 1$

$1 = 4$

$2 = 14$

$3 = 8$

$4 = 12$

$5 = 6$

$6 = 9$

The number of each capsule of the Galaxy space station, from 1 to 6, is such that for any particular capsule, the sum of the numbers of the capsules connected directly to it, equals the value corresponding to the numbers of that capsule as given in the list. For example a smaller space station is constructed as shown.

Space Station - Solution

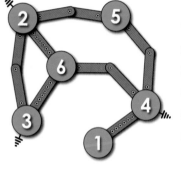

1 = 4

2 = 14

3 = 8

4 = 12

5 = 6

6 = 9

Screwy Problem

Rating 2 Points

Big Al bought 19 screws, some 1 inch long and some 1.5 inches long. He paid 3 cents more per screw for the longer screws and received no more than 10 cents change from $3.00, but did not know the exact prices. He had at least 5 screws of each type and could not have swapped around the numbers of each type. How many of each type were purchased and at what cost?

Screwy Problem - Solution

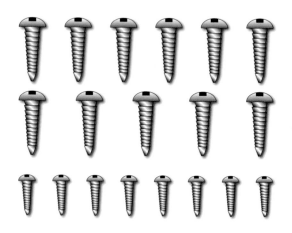

11 at 17 cents and 8 at 14 cents.

Let x be the number of 1.5 inch screws costing (t + 3) cents each. Then x(t + 3) + (19 − x)t = K where K cents is the total cost, just below 300 cents. Scrutinise and evaluate for minimum and maximum values of x, remembering that t must be a whole number. Eliminate solutions where the numbers of screws can be swapped around.

More Magic Squares

Rating 1 Point

Complete the magic square with each row, column
and diagonal adding up to 90. However you
may only use numbers made up from the digits 1, 2,
3 and 4 and all the numbers must be different.

More Magic Squares - Solution

31	12	34	13
33	14	32	11
24	43	1	22
2	21	23	44

Potty Problem

Rating 3 Points

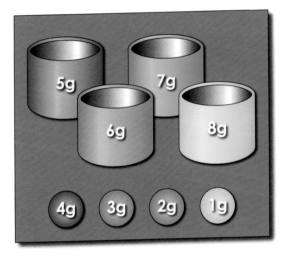

Can you place the same number of balls in each pot, without having the same color ball in the same color pot, so that each pot has at least one ball of every other color. The total weight of each pot and its contents must be the same. What is the minimum number of balls required in each pot to do this?

Potty Problem - Solution

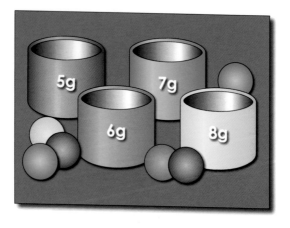

Red Pot + 7 blue, 1 green, 1 yellow = 29g
Blue Pot + 5 green, 1 yellow, 3 red = 29g
Green Pot + 3 yellow, 1 red, 5 blue = 29g
Yellow Pot + 1 red, 1 blue, 7 green = 29g

Number Crunching

Rating 1 Point

Complete the grid, using all but one of the numbers from 1 to 14, so that the middle row adds up to 31, the middle column adds up to 51 and all other rows, columns and diagonals add up to 19. The number 9 is given to start you on your way. What is the missing number?

Number Crunching - Solution

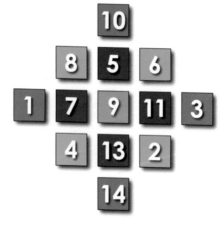

The missing number is 12.

Overall Scoring Page

Chapter	Score Card	Potential Score	Your Score
1	Page 8	40	
2	Page 54	40	
3	Page 100	40	
4	Page 146	40	
		GRAND TOTAL	

Anyone who has scored more than 120 points can afford to sit back and feel smug. Well done, you're in the top 25%!

Anyone who got between 80 and 120 points should be content knowing they got more than half of the puzzles correct.

Those with less than 80 points however, should turn over to page 192 for more information on Lagoon's other Brain-Boosting titles – you really should do a bit more practice!

OTHER BRAIN-BOOSTING TITLES AVAILABLE
FROM LAGOON BOOKS

BRAIN-BOOSTING SEQUENCE PUZZLES
(ISBN: 1902813537)

BRAIN-BOOSTING CRYPTOLOGY PUZZLES
(ISBN: 1902813545)

BRAIN BOOSTING VISUAL LOGIC PUZZLES
(ISBN: 1902813200)

BRAIN BOOSTING LATERAL THINKING PUZZLES
(ISBN: 1902813227)

BRAIN-BOOSTING CRYPTIC PUZZLES
(ISBN: 1902813219)

You can view our full range of puzzle books along
with the full collection of Lagoon Books on our website:

www.lagoongames.com

**LAGOON
BOOKS**